Let the Limericks Rock

1620

101 Limericks
The Story of the Pilgrims in Poetry

by
Sylvia D. Burke

To Oliver,
Enjoy reading
about our country's
christian history
With love,
Sylvia Burke
Hebrews 11:13
God bless you

Let the Limericks Rock

by
Sylvia D. Burke

The author can be contacted by email at
smburke1@msn.com

PUBLISHED BY:
BRENTWOOD ACADEMIC PRESS
COLUMBUS, GEORGIA 31904
WWW.BRENTWOODBOOKS.COM

Dedication

To my husband, H. Maurice Burke

To our children: David, Deborah and Daniel

To our grandchildren: Molly, Jordan, Jasmine, Abigail and Derek

(All are direct descendants of Governor William Bradford of the *Mayflower.*)

Acknowledgments

My granddaughter, Jordan Tiffani Jones, has always loved to draw. From the time she was old enough to hold a pencil she was busy drawing angels, mermaids, ballerinas, and pretty girls. Still a teenager, Jordan has developed her God-given talent and blessed me as the main illustrator of this book with her Pilgrims and Indians. It is amazing that the creative pictures she draws first originate in her mind, then she puts them on paper without even looking at a picture. Thank you, Jordan, you're awesome!

My long time friend and pastor, Dr. Paul Jehle, encouraged and advised me in several areas. As a respected historian he kept me accurate on Pilgrim facts. Thank you, Paul, for taking time from your busy schedule to help me with valuable suggestions.

Several family members were my proofreaders. Thanks go to Debbi Jones and Daniel Burke. Special thanks to my husband, Maurice, for his unending patience. I interrupted many TV football games and tennis matches asking, "Which sounds better...?" or "Can you think of a better word for...?" Maurice (Mo for short) also drew some of the illustrations.

Thank you David Burke for loaning me your laptop computer and helping with scanning and printing. Michael and Debbi Jones always came through with their computer expertise whenever I needed help. Debbi gave the title for the book. It rocks!

Foreword

The Pilgrim story should be retold in every home in America. It is not simply a story limited to the holiday of Thanksgiving, nor is it one that should be neglected as a footnote in the history of our nation. The Pilgrim story embodies faith, courage and character that are the cornerstones of our liberty as a nation. In this book of limericks, Sylvia Burke, a long time friend and a creative writer, unfolds the Pilgrim story in a way children and adults will enjoy, with serious reverence combined with humor. You will read it again and again, and learn the story that the next generation needs to understand that we might continue to be a nation blessed with freedom.

Dr. Paul Jehle,
Education Director, Plymouth Rock Foundation,
Senior Pastor, The New Testament Church

Understanding Limericks

Limericks are a unique kind of poetry. They consist of 5 lines. Lines 1, 2, and 5 rhyme with each other and usually contain eight syllables. Lines 3 and 4 rhyme and contain five or six syllables.

Some limericks are funny in nature, but I have chosen this style of poetry to tell the story of the Pilgrims, their courage, adventures and faith. Here is a sample of a limerick:

> I wrote this especially for you.
> Yes, the Pilgrim stories are true.
>   Sit down with the book,
>   And take a good look;
> Enjoy it whatever you do.

1

There once lived a people of fame;
The *Pilgrims*, their honorable name.
    You'll read in this book
    Of the journey they took
To America, from England they came.

2

Their story goes back many years.
The Pilgrims sometimes shed big tears.
   The challenge, you see,
   Was to live and be free
To worship their Lord without fears.

1620

3

There came a time in all England,
King James made a law in the land.
   All folks must obey,
   There was no other way
Than to honor the king's command.

1620

4

Only one church was approved by the king.
He was the head of it – not a good thing!
    The Pilgrims were sad;
    They longed to be glad,
To obey their conscience and sing.

1620

5

To the king's church they would not go.
"Separatists" they were called, you know.
　　They were chased by spies
　　With big, watchful eyes.
Some were jailed, adding problems and woe.

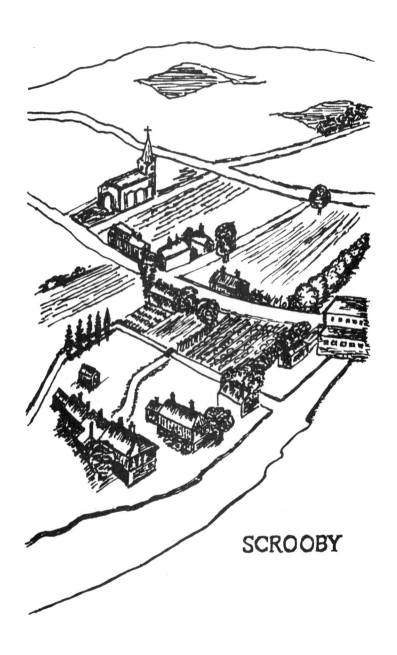

SCROOBY

6

In Scrooby town these faithful would meet;
At Brewster Manor, just down the street.
    That was their choice,
    'Cause they had no voice
In the government church – not so neat!

1620

7

They knew there was freedom in Holland.
Those who lived there said it was grand.
    To escape was a must.
    In God they would trust.
These Pilgrims were a courageous band!

1620

8

Without permission to leave was a crime.
They were betrayed and caught time after time.
    But with determined will,
    They kept trying until
They sailed to Holland with hardly a dime.

1620

9

Life in Holland in time went quite well.
In beautiful Leyden they chose to dwell.
　　Some learned a new trade.
　　A living was made;
Free to live by the Book – that was swell!

10

Twelve years passed by quickly, and then
They knew they must move once again.
 New problems they faced,
 That could not be erased;
So they prayed to know just where and when.

11

America was a big, unknown place,
Inhabited by the Indian race.
>   That's where they'd go.
>   Did they have enough dough?
They would trust in the Lord's hand of grace.

12

Merchant Adventurers from London town
Said they would help, and put money down.
    They struck up a deal;
    The terms seemed unreal.
This partnership oftentimes made them frown.

1620

13

Supplies for the trip they now sought.
The *Speedwell*, a small ship, they bought.
    It weighed sixty tons
    Without muskets or guns.
But would it be seaworthy, or not?

1620

14

They needed the *Mayflower* too.
It was bigger – that much they knew.
    This vessel was grand;
    Captain Jones in command.
It was time for their dream to come true.

15

Pastor John Robinson could not go,
But his love for his flock did show.
    They were one in prayer,
    And under God's care
For His blessings on them to bestow.

16

Big tears dropped from many an eye
As they hugged and then said, "Goodbye"
    To neighbor and friend
    They may not see again;
Then boarded the ship with a sigh.

1620

17

The *Mayflower* and *Speedwell* set sail.
This journey they knew must not fail.
　　But the *Speedwell* did leak,
　　And in less than a week,
They returned to the harbor quite pale.

18

The crew thought they'd fixed every leak,
Every problem and every creak.
    So they set sail again
    With hopeful men,
But the soundness of the ship proved bleak.

19

Once more, back to the harbor they went.
Precious days in delays had been spent.
    They must leave here fast,
    Before winter's cold blast.
All agreed – every lady and gent.

20

They had to abandon that ship.
Some folks now could not take the trip.
    Like birds of a feather,
    The rest flocked together
On the *Mayflower* – oh no! Would it tip?

1620

21

The passengers numbered one hundred two.
In addition, there was the ship's crew.
   Would there be enough food
   To feed this big brood?
I wonder did they eat much stew?

22

Once again the sails caught the breeze.
The Pilgrims were often on their knees.
    Daily they'd pray;
    Both night and day,
For safety through perilous seas.

1620

Are we there yet?

23

The children could not run and play.
They dreamed of their homes far away.
   "Are we almost there?"
   They'd ask, and then stare,
As the ship sailed on day after day.

1620

24

One day the main beam did crack.
Could they go on, or must they turn back?
    They knew what to do;
    With a great iron screw,
It was fixed, and the beam didn't lack.

1620

25

Young John Howland was blown overboard;
Lost his balance as the mighty wind roared.
   A miracle they say,
   He survived that day.
The truth of it cannot be ignored.

26

Liz Hopkins sang a sweet lullaby
So her new baby boy would not cry.
    Born on the ship,
    During the trip;
Named *Oceanus* – what a cute little guy!

27

The *Mayflower* was driven and tossed,
As the Atlantic they steadily crossed.
    Those old boards did creak,
    And the sky looked bleak;
Yet their faith in the Lord was not lost.

28

Sixty-six long days had passed.
From the crow's nest high on the mast;
  "Land Ho! Land Ho!"
  A sailor yelled, so
Very soon the anchor they'd cast.

29

The sunrise was glorious and bright.
Land was a marvelous sight!
    What joy they felt,
    As the Pilgrims knelt
And praised God in the warmth of His Light!

1620

30

Children smiled at what they could see.
Sand dunes stretched for miles endlessly.
    Sea gulls flew all about.
    A whale blew up a spout.
With excitement they giggled with glee!

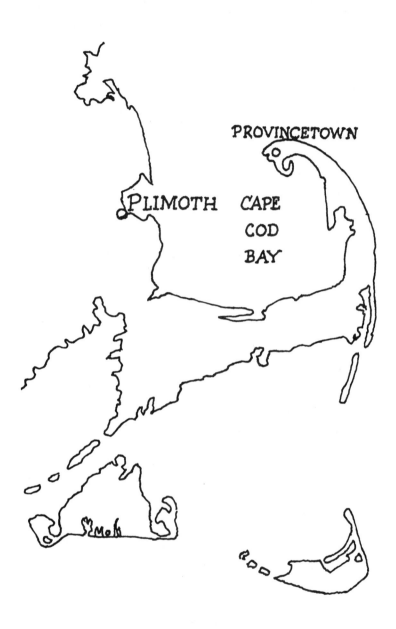

PROVINCETOWN

PLIMOTH   CAPE
COD
BAY

31

Wait a minute – to their dismay;
Captain Jones announced that they
    Were north of their goal,
    Near a sandbar or shoal.
It's not Virginia but Cape Cod Bay!

32

They resolved to sail south with care.
At that moment the wind was fair.
　　But it didn't take long
　　To know they were wrong;
To proceed – they just didn't dare!

33

They were caught in dangerous Pollack Rip.
The ship heaved and they feared they might flip.
    But thanks be to God,
    They sailed back to Cape Cod;
Extremely grateful for safety that trip.

34

Now what in the world should they do?
They talked with the captain and crew.
 All decided to stay;
 That was the best way.
In New England they'd start life anew.

35

But first there was business to do.
To each other they must remain true.
    Just laws must be made,
    And faithfully obeyed;
That would hold them together like glue.

1620

36

Elder Brewster said all should agree
For the good of the new colony.
   In the cabin they met;
   We must never forget
What they did to insure harmony.

37

The *Mayflower Compact* was signed.
This covenant was one of a kind.
    That November morn
    A government was born.
Men were one in spirit and mind.

Mayflower Compact

In the name of God, Amen. We whose names are underwritten, the loyal subjects of our dread sovereign Lord, King James, by the grace of God, of Great Britain, France and Ireland King, defender of the faith, etc., having undertaken, for the Glory of God, and advancement of the Christian faith, and honor of our King and country, a voyage to plant the first colony in the northern parts of Virginia, do by these presents solemnly and mutually in the presence of God, and one of another, covenant and combine ourselves together into a civil body politic, for our better ordering and preservation and furtherance of the ends aforesaid; and by virtue hereof to enact, constitute and frame such just and equal laws, ordinances, acts constitutions and offices from time to time, as shall be thought most meet and convenient for the general good of the colony, unto which we promise all due submission and obedience. In witness whereof, we have hereunder subscribed our names at Cape Cod, the 11th of November, in the year of the reign of our sovereign lord King James of England, France, and Ireland the eighteenth, and of Scotland the fifty-fourth. Anno Domino. 1620.

38

A governor now they must choose.
This man must hold fast to their views.
    He would serve for a year;
    It seemed perfectly clear
John Carver's the man – spread the news.

39

On the outside deck everyone stood.
Provincetown harbor looked very good.
    The anchor was cast,
    And the ship held fast.
They'd go ashore as soon as they could.

40

They needed to find just the right place
To settle – build homes – have a base.
    It must be secure,
    So they could endure;
Their concern could be seen on each face.

41

Sixteen men at noon went ashore
In the longboat to search and explore.
    Spring water they found
    Bubbling up from the ground.
Who could ask for anything more?

1620

42

The women had laundry to do.
Dirty clothes were more than a few.
   They washed in the stream,
   And worked as a team.
It was Monday – that custom grew.

1620

43

From this spot the men roamed the land.
Myles Standish was soldier in command.
    Often hungry and cold;
    What tales could be told,
As they marched along the Cape Cod sand.

1620

44

The Billington boys got in trouble.
With two of them, trouble was double.
    The ship they explored,
    Found the gunpowder stored,
And almost blew the ship into rubble!

1620

45

The hardships they faced were so real.
The cold, wintry wind they could feel.
    With little to eat,
     They would not retreat,
But pressed on, sometimes with no meal.

46

The shallop, a much smaller boat,
Was repaired, so now it would float.
    It was used by the men,
    Who searched once again,
As the sea mist froze on each coat.

1620

47

A settlement place soon they must find.
That thought weighed heavily on each mind.
 Just where should they go?
 They wanted to know,
As they left the *Mayflower* behind.

48

It began to rain and to snow.
They could not see where to go.
    Then the rudder broke;
    It wasn't a joke.
To an island they had to row.

49

Steering the shallop had been a chore.
It was dark when they stepped ashore.
 They were safe and blessed,
 So laid down to rest.
And my, could those weary men snore!

50

Clark's Island was empty they found.
And when they looked all around,
   A huge boulder they spied;
   There their clothes were dried,
By a fire they built on the ground.

51

Sunday morning dawned clear and bright.
They'd been safe through another night.
    So kept the Lord's Day
    In the usual way:
Praying, singing Psalms with all their might.

52

They had explored all around Cape Cod;
And now, by the Providence of God,
    Were led to a place,
    By His hand of grace,
At Plymouth the men gave a nod.

"For You are my Rock and my fortress;
therefore for Your Name's sake, lead me, and
guide me."   (Psalm 31:3)

53

The time was the 11ᵗʰ of December;
1620 – the year we remember.
   This brave little flock,
   Stepped on the Rock.
It was cold, not warm like September.

54

Did Indians live here by the sea?
If they did, then where could they be?
    No dwellings were there
    In the fresh salt air.
Now this was a big mystery.

55

I'll tell you now just what they found:
There were cleared cornfields all around,
    With brooks and springs,
    And other fine things;
Like rich soil to grow crops in the ground.

56

Back to the *Mayflower* they sailed,
As an easterly wind prevailed;
    To tell the good news,
    A place they'd soon choose,
Because their searching had not failed.

1620

57

In a cradle rocked Peregrine White.
This newborn was a precious sight.
   The White's knew their son
   Was the first English one
To be born in New England's light.

1620

58

The women were glad that their men
Were back on the *Mayflower* again.
    They heard with delight,
    Their stories that night;
As they told of the places they'd been.

59

One unhappy event I must relate.
William Bradford lost his helpmate.
  Dorothy fell overboard
  In a storm as it poured.
December 17 – what a sad date!

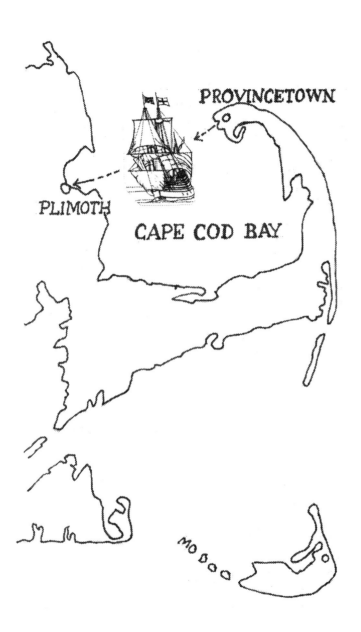

PROVINCETOWN

PLIMOTH

CAPE COD BAY

60

The Pilgrims must be on their way.
They weighed anchor the very next day.
    The masts unfurled,
    In the New World,
As they sailed across Cape Cod Bay.

61

Into Plymouth Harbor they came,
Believing a new life they'd obtain.
    This place was the best,
    Compared to the rest.
That thought became perfectly plain.

62

It was here they decided to stay;
On a hill high above the Bay.
    What a wonderful thing!
    No more wandering;
They could settle down – oh! happy day.

63

They knew it was smart to plan well,
Before any trees they should fell.
   The families drew lots
   For the places of their plots.
Now their plans all started to gel.

64

In the harbor the *Mayflower* moored.
The women and children lived aboard.
    The men crossed the Bay;
    As day after day,
Their building could not be ignored.

65

With great fervor axes were swung.
All men worked, both old and young
    They labored and sweat,
    Often cold and wet;
Determined, to their dreams they clung.

66

At night most went back to the ship.
Sometimes winter winds would whip.
    As the shallop crossed,
    In the surf it was tossed;
Making for a dangerous trip.

67

First a common house, and a fort
Were built, as their journals report.
    Each served as a place
    To help them feel safe;
Shelters where they could resort.

The Pilgrims who died the first winter were buried at night in unmarked graves so the Indians would not know how many had died. In later years gravestones were used.

68

The first winter many fell ill.
It took all their courage and will.
    Half of them died,
    Their friends at their side;
Laid to rest on Burial Hill.

1620

69

Week after week passed on by,
And those axes continued to fly.
    Then houses took shape,
    Right there near the Cape,
With thatched roofs they knew how to tie.

70

Through the woods a visitor came by.
What a surprise as he said, "Hi!
    Welcome English, me Samoset."
    On that day two worlds met.
They became friends, no one can deny.

1620

71

Samoset answered questions all day.
His English was poor – that was okay.
    The mystery was solved,
    Where they were involved;
The Patuxet tribe had all passed away.

72

Massasoit was the sachem or chief.
His meeting with the Pilgrims was brief.
    They talked for a while
    In Indian style,
And promised each other no grief.

1620

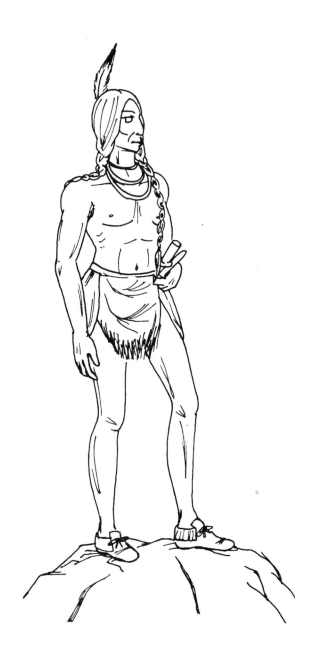

73

The points of the treaty were defined;
Before the agreement was signed.
    It lasted fifty years,
    Reducing their fears.
During visits they left weapons behind.

1620

74

Squanto was interpreter and guide.
His influence went far and wide.
　　This Indian brave
　　Was a gift God gave.
In Plymouth he stayed by their side.

75

The *Mayflower* must now depart.
Captain Jones was ready to start.
    It had been their base;
    A safe, secure place.
They waved good-by with a heavy heart.

76

Plantation work started at dawn,
So progress moved steadily on.
    Then John Carver died.
    With sadness they cried;
Their beloved governor was gone.

1620

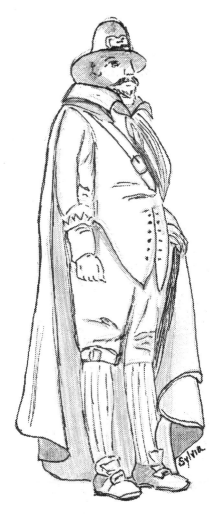

Statue of William Bradford
Plymouth Harbor

77

William Bradford was chosen to lead;
A godly man without malice or greed.
    They knew that young Will
    Had the wisdom and skill
To govern; so to him they gave heed.

78

Squanto proved to be helpful indeed.
He showed them how to plant seed.
    "Put a fish in the ground,
    Then the seeds all around."
Corn flourished in their time of need.

79

Spring rains came, then summer sun.
The Pilgrims had little time for fun.
    They worked in their field;
    Each corn stalk would yield
Three ears when the growing was done.

1620

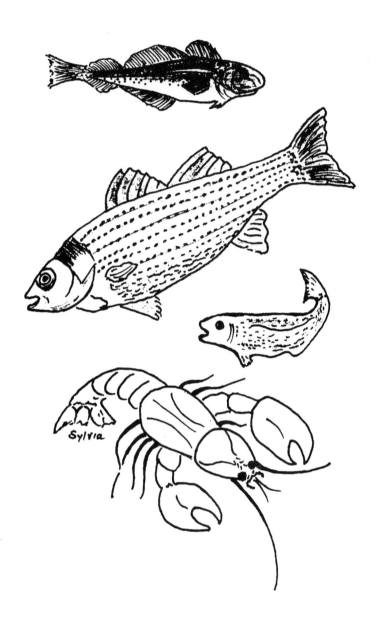

Sylvia

80

The bay teemed with all kinds of fish;
As much as anyone could wish:
    Herring, mackerel and cod,
    Even flounder and scrod.
Each catch made a delicious dish.

1620

81

In the marshes and woods they found
Wild turkeys, geese and deer to abound.
    They hunted and fished
    Whenever they wished.
Health improved; some might gain a pound.

1620

82

Harvest season was drawing near.
They had reason to be of good cheer.
    The storehouse was filled
    With corn to be milled.
So much had been done in one year.

83

Such blessings could not be ignored.
With rejoicing, they praised the Lord.
    They'd rest from their labors,
    And invite their neighbors
To celebrate. No one would be bored.

84

Preparations got underway
For this feast one November day.
    The menu was planned;
    It would be so grand!
Now what would the Indians say?

85

Squanto went with the invitation
To Chief Massasoit and his nation.
    Since they loved to eat,
    It would be a treat
To come to the big celebration.

86

The women cooked flavorful food
In a happy and joyful mood.
    Wild turkeys and geese
    Were roasted with grease,
As juicy clams simmered and stewed.

87

Now Massasoit came to the feast
With many braves – ninety at least.
    His men shot five deer
    In the woods quite near,
So the supply of food increased.

88

Before they all started to eat,
Elder Brewster rose to his feet,
    And thanked God above
    For His bountiful love.
They were free; and freedom was sweet!

89

The Indians were glad they had come.
There was food enough for each one.
    They performed in dance,
    With loud, tribal chants.
Myles Standish put on drills to a drum.

90

The first Thanksgiving lasted three days.
Then their guests went their several ways.
 Their friendship confirmed;
 As everyone learned,
Being generous and kind always pays.

91

Each Sunday they all marched to church,
Walking through the pine trees and birch.
    With Bible in hand,
    Free in this land;
For hours in the Scriptures they'd search.

92

It was almost a year to the date,
The ship *Fortune* arrived – it was late.
    Not thoughtful or wise,
    They brought no supplies;
Not one barrel of flour or a crate.

1620

93

The season for planting was past.
Pilgrims knew what they had must last.
    Still they shared their food
    In a charitable mood;
Knowing winter was coming on fast.

94

The Pilgrims sent back goods and furs
To the London men they called, "Sirs."
    That was the best way,
    Their debt to repay,
To the Merchant Adventurers.

95

From time to time other ships came.
Some of those men did not think the same.
    They settled elsewhere,
    Not seeming to care;
Cheating the Indians to their shame.

96

But this kind did not long endure,
Because their motives weren't pure.
　　Back to England they went,
　　From where they'd been sent.
The Indians were happy for sure.

William Bradford's 1592 Geneva Bible

97

The beginnings of this nation
Go back to Plymouth Plantation.
    That brave little band
    Took a valiant stand;
They fought for their faith, and they won!

1620

Pilgrim Mother Monument

98

We still celebrate *Forefathers' Day*.
There are monuments along the way.
    The Plantation's restored.
    Mayflower 2ⁿᵈ is moored
In the harbor of Plymouth Bay.

1620

99

The Forefathers' Monument stands high
On a hill, on Allerton Street nearby.
    Eighty-one feet in height;
    It's an awesome sight.
There *"Faith"* points her arm to the sky.

100

"One small candle may light a thousand."
Shine that light so glorious and grand.
    Governor Bradford's quote,
    Is in the book he wrote.
That small beginning spread through the land.

1620

101

Now the Pilgrim story you know;
Lessons of devotion they show.
        We too must hold fast,
        Remembering the past,
So flames of faith and freedom still glow.

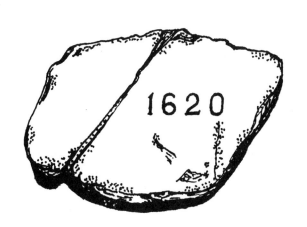

Bibliography

Atwood, William Franklin. *The Pilgrim Story* (Plymouth, Mass.: The Memorial Press, 1940, rev. 1958)

Bradford, William. *Of Plymouth Plantation: Bradford's History of the Plymouth Settlement 1608-1650* (San Antonio, Texas: The Vision Forum in association with Mantle Ministries: Bulverde, Texas, 1998)

Daugherty, James. *The Landing of the Pilgrims* (New York: Random House, 1950, 1978, 2001)

Fiore, Jordan D. *Mourt's Relation: A Journal of the Pilgrims of Plymouth* (Plymouth, Massachusetts: Plymouth Rock Foundation, 1985)

Jehle, Paul. *Plymouth in the Words of Her Founders: A Visitor's Guide to America's Hometown* (San Antonio, Texas: Vision Forum Ministries, 2002)